Chick-a-boo!

By Amanda Brandon

Illustrated by
Natasha Rimmington

Hen is in a huff.

Chick is missing.

She looks for him.

The farm is big.

Hen sees Dog run down the hill.

Chick-a-boo! Chick runs too.

Come back, Chick!

Hen cannot get him.

Chick sits in the weeds.

Rabbit hops up and...

...chick-a-boo! Chick zooms off.

Hen cannot get him.

Cat taps her foot and...

...chick-a-boo!

Chick shoots in the air.

Hen cannot get him.

Duck swims up.

Chick-a-boo!

Chick hops on his back.

Hen cannot get him.

Chick needs to sleep.

He sees a barn.

Hen needs to sleep too.

She looks in the barn and...

...she sees Chick.

Then...

...Cow lets out a deep MOO!

Chick jumps up.

He zooms into...

...Hen's big wings.

Chick-a-boo!

Hen and Chick hug tight.

Thank you, Cow!

Quiz

1. Why is Hen looking for Chick?

a) He is sleeping

b) He is missing

c) He is flying

2. The farm is _____.

a) big

b) fun

c) small

3. Whose back does Chick hop onto?

a) Rabbit

b) Dog

c) Duck

4. Cow lets out a _____ MOO!

a) high

b) low

c) deep

5. Where does Chick zoom into?

a) Hen's big wings

b) Cow's soft ears

c) The pile of hay

Turn over for answers

Pink
Red
Yellow
Blue
Green
Orange
Turquoise
Purple
Gold
White

Book Bands for Guided Reading

The Institute of Education book banding system is a scale of colours that reflects the various levels of reading difficulty. The bands are assigned by taking into account the content, the language style, the layout and phonics. Word, phrase and sentence level work is also taken into consideration.

Maverick Early Readers are a bright, attractive range of books covering the pink to white bands. All of these books have been book banded for guided reading to the industry standard and edited by a leading educational consultant.

To view the whole Maverick Readers scheme, visit our website at www.maverickearlyreaders.com

Or scan the QR code above to view our scheme instantly!

Quiz Answers: 1b, 2a, 3c, 4c, 5a